# a stranger journey

written by Andrea Gatopoulos
photos by Antonio Morra

When I turned twenty I made these wishes: by thirty I wanted to write a book, make a film and have a child. I was a kid and now I'm definitely not a kid anymore. I made many films, I wrote a book and it was my sister who had a son. Like all things, when you grab them you then realize that they have changed in shape and consistency, like a kind of soap bar that slips through your hands. What does it mean to make a film? Because you learn that it's easy to put images one after another, put titles on them and say: this is a film. But is it really a film, then? Does it really grant that wish? And when do images become a film and who can tell? The others? A festival? How many of the films I have made are truly films and how many are just sequences, montages? It seems to me that the desire to make a film is a naive desire, it is a desire of a twenty-year-old kid. And so is writing a book or painting a picture or taking a photograph. Chimeras for teenagers. Certainly not like having a child, which is the only thing I haven't done. In the end I seem to have understood that it wasn't important to make just any film, but to be clear about one's obsessions, the promises they make and the consequences they have. I wanted to be a director, it would have been enough for me to be any director and now instead I would like to be a particular type of director or perhaps not even a director, but simply someone with something to say that doesn't have that obscene and opportunistic aftertaste of the things of our world. And so with all the other things in life. I'm turning thirty and everything has changed. For some reason I'm much less interested in vague desires. It's likely that making my last film contributed a lot to this change, because it's been a strange journey. I did it with Antonio Morra, who took photos in the many moments of pause. His photos are the perfect excuse to talk about it and most importantly they are very beautiful.

We departed on October 23rd, 2022 from Milan Malpensa towards San Francisco, California.

I need to archive, watch, edit and subtitle the footage every day. I need to stay in one room for a long time, especially at the beginning of a shoot. Antonio was bored, so one day he took David's car and ended up I don't know where. Instead of taking the subway he walked around and from what I understand from his stories in San Francisco that's a big mistake. When he returned he told me that he had taken a beautiful photo of the Golden Gate Bridge and that he had been afraid of being stabbed. That he ended up on a street where everyone looked like drugged zombies who looked at him badly. Thank God they didn't stab Antonio. I love him and moreover the movie would have finished before it started.

For me there is something very disturbing about Palo Alto. Even though we are in the heart of Silicon Valley, I immediately felt a sense of danger, the presence of a ruthless concept. The houses so neatly arranged one after the other, with the lawns mowed, the electric cars moving along the road crawling like ghosts without raising a breath of dust, certain apartment buildings that look like banks with revolving doors, no one walking on the sidewalk or talking on the phone with a loud voice or simply looking out of a window minding other people's business, homeless people dragging trolleys looking at the ground and stopping to sigh on bus stop benches, supermarkets where the vegetables are as perfect as they were printed in 3D and cost an arm and a leg, cute little squirrels jumping around or run over on the side of the road, rigid and forgotten, no one looking at you in the face, everyone just going straight on... They all seem to fanatically serve some God, who is definitely not my own. I sometimes wondered what would happen if I touched one of them, what texture would they have? Would it be a cardboard cutout, an ever-standing, an NPC? Moreover, I was deathly afraid of the police. For the stories that we hear in Europe, but also for a natural instinct, for the effect it had on me here. I felt like a stranger, I felt no trust. We went shopping and immediately came back upstairs with a sense of fear and in the evening we played Magic The Gathering and watched One Piece while I made copies of the footage, before I could watch them again to subtitle them. Antonio took two photos: one of the driveway next to the Airbnb where we slept, which, seeing it now, seems to me to represent the last five safe meters before plunging into that liminal order, and one of the house behind ours, with a crow hovering above us in circles. It was full of birds that looked at us turning their heads to the side, as if we were an oddity. They were right.

As a child, in Pescara, the covers of English books usually had a photo of a Chinese man, a black man, an Arab, a white man with brown hair and another with freckles and red hair, and all of them were smiling and happy together. At the time it seemed like an impossible gathering, an unattainable melting pot, because in Pescara they were all white and spoke dialect at best and for me that was the world, or rather, I was always the strange one, with the Greek surname. But Stanford is exactly like that. I don't know if I could ever get used to something like this, sometimes I think that the concept of home fossilizes before the age of five or six, and that it is, after all, an aesthetic concept that has to do with the shape, with the colours, with the smells of things and that once you have learned what home is for you - or what home is not, or what it means not to have it, or what it means to dream of it - then you carry that sort of feeling or idea with you forever, or in any case it takes you more and more effort to get used to anything else. I know for a fact that I could never feel at home in a place like Stanford. Not here, not in Palo Alto, not, probably, in California. Every time I leave it I miss the everyday Roman chaos, the bad smells, the rudeness, the seagulls that tear apart rats near garbage cans and then let out terrifying screams, the fireworks from the next block that mean that cocaine has arrived. There is something horrendously tender in all this, which here disappears in a polite and codified and therefore substantially fragile harmony. This photo was taken in front of the Green Library, where David founded the David Rumsey Map Center. We shot so many scenes for the film here, most of which were cut. It makes me sorry because they were very interesting.

We started shooting the film almost without warning. Once the camera and the microphones were set up, I said hello Steve, nice to meet you, I'm Andrea, okay, go ahead, and we went to record. I told David to simply go and tell Steve what he thought of the work he was doing: Steve was building a spinning wheel with a copy of Urbano Monti's planisphere on it as the cartographer had always dreamed of, not separated in sheets, but merged in a single print. A wonderful and unique map, the oldest map of the entire world, a great work of art of humanity, which Monti managed to draw without ever leaving Italy. They were placing it in the corner of a large study hall and library at Stanford. It was a gift from David to the university. I had forbidden David to come near me before filming, so we were able to capture the genuineness of his enthusiasm. While he was touching the map and the various pieces of the wheel he seemed very enthusiastic and tender, like a sweet child with its favourite thing and for me this was enough to confirm the success of the scene, the tenderness of it. In the following days, the students didn't seem to care that much about it. David and Christina from Map Center sat down to find a strategy that would stimulate them to play it, because they were all in awe of it. Maybe they thought the map was too beautiful to touch? Maybe it happens because it is a generation used to seeing all the wonders of the world behind the display cases of a museum or behind the glass of a telephone, and they would never think something beautiful is actually meant to be touched.

A person used to living in a one bedroom apartment cannot help but feel a certain form of shock when sleeping for a few days in a house like this. David offered to let us sleep in his home, in a mid-nineteenth-century four-story Victorian building that was once a church with a nunnery and a nursery. David keeps portraits of his mother as a child, of his old relatives, of his dead, hanging in certain corners. They felt like ghosts, which always seem gentle if you know them, but kind of territorial if you don't. Furthermore, the house is made of wood and creaks in the wind. I'm not used to such a big house, it seemed uncontrollable to me, evil could enter from any of those hundred windows and those four entrance doors and all the rooms had more than one entrance. The first evening we were scared and couldn't sleep. We wondered why we didn't stay in our little Airbnb. I fell asleep and dreamed of monsters. In the morning I realized that I was alive and I calmed down. Whatever presence haunted those places seemed not to be interested in killing me.

At times during filming I wondered how David was feeling. The way we met was very twenty-first century. I ended up on his site, I liked it, I watched a couple of interviews, I liked them, I said to myself: okay, I was looking for a person like this, a story like this, I'm going to contact him and I did. We had a video call while I was preparing the materials to try Venice Biennale College's program with another project, another production, another life that didn't come true because they didn't take me. From the first moment I had the feeling that he was me and I was him. I always had the impression that people could fall into a maximum of a hundred archetypes, which whoever made us thought was enough to ensure enough variety. He and I are definitely children of the same archetype. We have the same ways and we have the same scruples, the same way of dealing with people, and the same relationship with ambition. In fact David had started as a photographer, as a student of Walker Evans, then he was an artist until he was thirty and then he had a daughter and decided to change life. I'm about to turn thirty and sometimes it occurs to me to do both. Will I ever be eighty? And at eighty will a boy from overseas feel like he belongs to the same archetype as me? Will I remember this strange coincidence, or will it go unnoticed, slip away like the keystone of every theory of the world, which promptly falls from one's hands like sand?

There are houses that have a powerful aura, and others that are insignificant. You feel it immediately, it's in the smell, it's in the invisible pattern drawn by the arrangement of the objects, by the criterion that preceded them. David's house is an incredible, intense house. In the basement there is part of his collection of maps and geography books, atlases, tools, instruments and toys related to cartography. It is regularly filled with maps until it bursts, then David, once the objects have been catalogued, donates everything to Stanford so that it can make room for a new collection. Accumulating. Letting go. Everything was tastefully arranged and spoke to me as if in a sort of soft choir. I thought about the tsukumogami, the spirits who according to a Japanese belief inhabit objects that are more than a hundred years old. Maybe we really were surrounded! According to belief, if the owner of the object had treated it well in life, the spirit would have been kind and beneficent. Knowing how much that collection had been loved, I therefore definitely felt safe. It is very likely that this photo of Antonio was taken by me. It was either me or a tsukumogami.

An abandoned kitchen, probably out of use for years. It's in the basement of David's house, a house where even an entire room can get lost. At this time, and only at this time probably, given the inclination, a ray of light entered it. Antonio noticed it and took this photograph. I never entered this room, it had nothing to do with my film and while I was in that house I didn't even break into a drawer, let alone a room. I have a very vague memory of it. At one point during filming, David confessed to me that he had an old phone with voicemail recorded with his late mother's voice. He told me he left it somewhere in the house. We searched far and wide for it, everywhere, and we couldn't find it. At that moment I asked myself whether such a house could literally swallow objects, keep them in the dark for an immemorial time, hide them jealously, seize them. Perhaps there are houses that feed on time and others that always remain in a sort of infinite present, without past and without future? Maybe there was some spirit involved here too? There is something deeply sweet and deeply desperate about it all and I wonder what it would feel like to die knowing that you have to leave behind a place that holds all your memories of a lifetime. I don't know, because I don't own a house and I can't afford it and it's a great pain in my life, but above all I don't know because I'm not dead yet, I'll let you know when the time comes.

Now that I think about it, we looked for that phone everywhere but not in this kitchen, and now I wonder if perhaps one day David might have stopped on the threshold of this kitchen, after so many years without using it, and chose it to listen to one more once that voice, perhaps then forgetting the box there, forever…

I shot this scene with David with his back to the camera, because I knew he would speak for a long time, and in this way I could cut it later. It was the scene in which he called his wife Abby to tell her that he had thought about everything, about his twenty years as a real estate developer during the economic boom of San Francisco and had left art aside, about how he had decided to quit at fifty, how it had taken a gigantic truck to take away all those papers and send them to the shredder, tons of paperwork, bureaucracy, non-life that accumulates and becomes money, comfort, this four-story house in San Francisco, his house of wood and glass in Muir Beach, his house in the desert in the middle of nowhere, his house that a hundred years ago was a fisherman's house in the disappeared village of MacKinnons Brook, his endless collection of wonderful maps, and yet, he said on the phone, those twenty years were a hole in time, twenty strange years, underwater, with bated breath, waiting for life, which came when he finally stopped making money and dedicated himself again to his mind, to maps, to art and started to breathe again. This is all a funny mystery. Some things fill your soul and some have teeth and they devour it. This is the truth. We must be careful of both one and the other. A certain type of hunger is always lurking. On the one hand there is internal emptiness and on the other the emptiness in the stomach. Both can make you truly miserable or even a real piece of shit. It's dangerous.

In the last room of the basement where he keeps his home collection, David has a gigantic flat screen, I think a hundred-inch one. He sits in front of it at a very inadvisable distance, so much so that you have to turn your head to look at the corners of the screen. It seems as if he is suspended in front of a body of water. If he could, he would stick his head inside, to finally live not on top of his maps, but inside. Thus arranged, he gets as close as possible, but when it's time to click the menu, due to the inclination, he can't read the writing at the top and has to stand up. Playing Second Life in front of such a screen, in that position, causes the type of alienation that leads you to think that digital reality is the main one and not vice versa. When you stop the world seems very slow and disjointed and you feel like you're going crazy. Then everything goes back to normal like after a fever.

We wanted to shoot a scene inside Meta Horizon, the virtual reality created by Zuckerberg. As usual, we set up the camera, started recording, and let Nate teach David how to create an avatar of himself. David, with the visor on his head, immediately looked for how to get a hat and glasses and then decided to get a piercing like his grand-daughter's. We watched what he saw from the stream on the monitor in the other room. Meta Horizon is a horrible, liminal and disturbing place, where the avatars have no legs and seem to smile like strangers smile in nightmares. To all intents and purposes, it seems more like a sort of gloomy asylum in an afterlife where everyone is already dead than an alternative reality. All the references to childhood and baby games contribute to creating a strange sense of ghostly imprisonment. On top of that you can't do anything and it's very boring. As you walk you hear the voices of other avatars as if they were both underwater and inside a coffin. In the main square of that strange paper city there was an avatar with dreadlocks who tried to teach everyone how to send a ball into a basket, but the ball was rigged and all you had to do was shoot it and it went by itself. He celebrated anyway every time and I asked myself why. David tried to talk to someone, he greeted tenderly, but the others ignored him. He probably didn't have the courage to stop, take the visor off and ask us what all this was for so as not to ruin the scene. There were also two avatars of a woman and a child, probably her son. At one point the child said: "Mom, this place is scary." and his mother muted the microphone for him. I thought: if reality is a hallucination, virtual reality is the hell of the mind. The scene was bad and boring and we cut it.

In his home in Muir Beach, north of San Francisco, you can stretch out on this sofa placed in a completely glassed-in niche overlooking the Pacific. Squinting through the fog you see Chinese ships taking to the sea and sinking into the nothingness in which they will sail for weeks. At lunchtime an amazing light arrives and fills the house with bright and geometric prisms, and you feel lucky. At five o'clock, before the sun goes down, flocks of pelicans return to their nests for the night. For weeks after filming ended, from here, David sent me photos of sunrises and sunsets over the gulf below. I looked at the buildings in Rome and thought where the fuck did I make my nest. Pelicans live better.

I can't understand how in most of the photos taken by Antonio I don't have glasses. Did I always wear contact lenses? I don't think so. Glasses or no glasses, certain objects become like parts of the body. One certainly doesn't have to think about whether or not he brought an ear with him. So it is with my glasses. There are very few photos of me wearing glasses, yet I always have them on my face. Am I the one hiding them or are they the ones hiding? However, I have never understood why I love so much to see a woman wearing glasses, not just any glasses, but short-sighted glasses like mine. I have always linked glasses to the courage to live with one's defects, which I absolutely do not have. Perhaps a dream is nothing more than the unexpressed desire within us. This is why we are always ashamed of our most absurd dreams. My stupidest dream is a world where all women wear glasses.

David and RJ Andrews talking about data and statistics.
David and Paul Saffo talking about the dead in the future.
David and Leon, eight years old, trying virtual reality.
David unpacking a Rizzi- Zannoni map and enjoying looking at it.
David taking a bath outside in the hot Jacuzzi as the storm rolls in.
David in a bathrobe sipping tea.
David telling Stace about how a student thought he was already dead .
David returning to his home on Beulah Street.
David asking Drake for help fixing his website.
David discussing the future of teaching with Julie.

We cut a lot of scenes and we did the right thing.

Yet it is a great pain to consign an image to oblivion, to do it on purpose, we who are those who create images to save them from nothingness. But after a few years it became clear to me that making cinema is just knowing how to choose, so knowing how to do it perhaps means nothing more than enduring this pain without whining too much.

In any case it was time to move. From San Francisco we went to the Smoke Creek Desert, in Nevada. The closest town, about forty kilometers away, was Gerlach, the base for those who go to live at Burning Man and disappear from the map forever. David had the car checked, filled a thermos with some tea, took a pack of lemon Ricolas and a couple of protein bars. We loaded onto the back of the truck a musical synthesizer that he and his companions built at Yale during the years of Pulsa, his collective of artists who among other things had an exhibition at MoMA in which David was photographed by Irving Penn and ended up in Vogue, parallel lives, interrupted lives, roads that could have gone in one direction but instead went in another and who knows how mine will go, now that I am exactly the same age as he was at the time when he lived in a common in New Haven and was an artist and now he is eighty years old and a collector of maps after having been a real estate developer with a mustache and a jacket for twenty years. Everything can happen. Anyway, the one in our car was one of the first synthesizers in the history of music. It was in good cosmetic condition, but it no longer worked because it was almost sixty years old. We were taking it to Kevin Braheny Fortune, the composer who lent us the extraordinary and unknown music that would then accompany the ending of the film, *Lullaby for the Hearts of Space*, a piece that is the demonstration that in an artistic profession quality is only one of the ingredients of success and often it is not even the fundamental one, oblivion is always around the corner with its inexplicable criteria and we must fight it ferociously by following the strange constellations of beauty. David was the one driving and we trusted him. To get there we crossed the Sierra Nevada, where a snowstorm was raging. We got stuck in a lot of freight truck traffic because the police wanted to check drivers for I don't know what . Then we met Kevin, who came down a mountain path to meet us. The snow was knee-deep. He took the synthesizer, we shook hands, we realized that it was too cold and we each went off on our own.

Once we passed the Sierra Nevada, which acted as a bastion against the wind and disturbances of the Pacific, we filled up with gas in Reno, on the border between California and Nevada, a city that was resurgent because Tesla had moved its headquarters there. Here the earth began to change color, to turn yellow, the evergreen forests began to give way to artemisia bushes and clusters of succulents, the temperature showed no signs of rising and yet a desert began, a cold desert. On the road towards the North the cities became small inexplicable agglomerations, a few smokestacks in the void, motels and service stations, and everything seemed to branch out from the infinite strip of asphalt that ran like a cancerous vein across a strip of yellow and hairless flesh. We saw the first ranches, horses and cows, a dog running madly in the middle of a prairie where the meadow was a sort of hoary and fragile down, a railway line climbing the distant ridges whose freight trains would arrive to the other side of the United States after days of travel. We listened to Sirius XM, the radio playing some hits from the 70s or 80s that David really enjoyed like *Stuck in the Middle with You* by Fleetwood Mac, Antonio slept and I was sleepy as well but I was ashamed of sleeping and leaving David alone to drive, even though sometimes I did it anyway. In fact there are no photos of this part of the journey, there are only vague images in my head, memories that my brain will continue to modify as it pleases to cloak them in magic, so I will never know if Pyramid Lake, sacred to the Indians, was really so blue, a blue that would take your breath away and I will never know if the faces of those few people that we met, looking strangely at the cars while panning their heads from left to right were really so fascinating, I'll never be sure if living in nothingness really gave your appearance that sinister and atavistic something that everyone seemed to have painted on their faces. The only thing I know is that that endless nowhere had already swallowed me up. Then, at a certain point, amidst a lot of chatter, after hundreds of straight miles, David turned left and we arrived at Parker Ranch.

In '96 David bought a wasteland in the middle of the Smoke Creek Desert from a failed rancher. He had just stopped working in real estate and started his new life as a map collector. He had done some calculations and was convinced that, given the presence of numerous hot water springs in the surrounding area, if he dug a well the water would gush out. So it was, and from a wasteland Parker Ranch became a small oasis in the desert, with running water. David and Michael, his longest-standing friend who as if on purpose was a painter like my most trusted friend - again on the subject of archetypes - went to take three hundred trees from an evergreen forest and replanted them personally, one by one, around the pool of water that was created. In a clearing of land in the center of the pool David built his house. Michael built his own a little further. Their first neighbor lived forty kilometers away and hunting on the ranch was prohibited. Here, silence was better than silence. It was a rarefied and serene nature, where animals lived their lives sheltered from men and history, a life of hunting, farting, rape, childbirth, illness and death, under the light of stars that died millions of years ago, far away from the curiosity and madness of human beings. David comes here several times a year, takes a walk in the desert, rows the boat towards the center of the lake that he has created and lies on his stomach to look at the stars or takes a bath near the jet of hot water. This is how you go back to the animal dimension, where you are alone with the cosmos and things become clearer and more tangible or darker and senseless but in any case they take a clear direction instead of this unbearable vagueness. Antonio was entranced by that place, he told me hey where did you take me, it's an incredible place, and disappeared for a while to take photographs. Understandable, given that he lives in Milan.

It was a house made of wood, glass and sheet metal, modeled on the old train stations of the West, inside which there was always an incredible light that often took on golden or greenish hues. There was a bedroom upstairs, where David slept, and one downstairs that I left to Antonio. I took the sofa in the living room. At night, when darkness came, everything was lit up with a blue moonlight reflected on the white desert and you could observe nature as far as the eye could see, the fumes of the hot spring rising above the still water of the pools, clear like it was midday. Rabbits and hares, small deer and owls, shadows that slipped through the vegetation, shadows that could be anything, animals as spirits or the ghosts of my grandparents who came to snoop to find out what the hell I was doing in that place, how I ended up there, in a place that I would never have seen in my life because it didn't exist in any tourist guide, on any map, a place where only cinema could take me and this was enough to make it worth it both for me and the ghosts who continued to see the world through me.

The next morning the light of dawn woke me up. I sat up and looked out at the steaming pools of water. They were full of ducks bathing. Then I noticed that the house was surrounded by deer that had come to drink. I stood up and went to the window, trying not to make any noise, but of course they heard me. I expected them to run away, but instead they remained calm. In that place, no human being had ever harmed them, after all they had nothing to fear. I waited for Antonio to wake up, but then I saw him already sneaking through the vegetation to take photos of the deer. Who knows what this fawn thought when he looked at the camera, what a strange smell, what a strange behavior this furless creature has, what strange colors, what the hell does he want from me, he should go fuck himself, maybe it's better to run away.

I later explored the area on my own. Near the water I found a dead deer. There was a bloody circular hole in his side. It could have been a bullet or the beak of a large bird, but it was more likely that some fool had shot it and that the deer had then walked to the pool to die in a place where it felt safe and protected. David got angry because it was obvious that someone was coming to hunt in those parts. I wondered how one kills for taste, how different other people's minds are, what goes through their heads, but above all what divides us? An insurmountable ravine, or just the distance of a hug or a handshake? Certainly a film like mine in all likelihood would not have bridged that gap. What is the point of cinema, this is the question of questions, it is the question to which we have no answer and we work to give ourselves one for our whole lives, and then we die.

The desert is full of paths. Who traced them and why is unknown. They're not going anywhere. They start without a reason and end the same way, you simply lose track of them in the nothingness. Yet someone has walked them for some reason. Probably hunters or ranch cowboys gone to dust a hundred years ago. Once every five years a random walker comes to remind one of those paths that it is a path, tramples on the low plants of Artemisia Tridentata, makes up that little space that will suggest the presence of a road to the next person. And so until the end of human time, a chain of walkers scattered throughout eternity will pass along the paths that Antonio, David and I have followed to go who knows where, who knows if to shoot another film. We will never know anything about each other, just like those disconnected roads.

Lesson learned: there is nothing colder than a cold desert. When the sun begins to sink behind the distant mountains, everything turns a shocking pink. It is a light of alarm, of warning. In the dark the temperature drops fifteen degrees in two hours, and a face-eating wind comes, showing you exactly what you are, compared to that landscape: a crumb of flesh in the universe, perfectly useless and digestible. Antonio and I went far away to shoot the opening credit sequence and we stayed longer than we should have. David had stayed home and the sun was going down. I thought: he's surely worried, and now he's going to take the car and come to look for us. So it was. As we went down to our Jeep with the tripod and the case of lenses we heard the sound of a car. It was David. He caught up to us, rolled down the window and tried to mask his apprehension: "I wanted to check on you guys!" he said smiling. Then he turned the car around and we all went home for dinner. David grilled a slice of salmon and Antonio made rice with broccoli and toasted bread with butter. We drank a Californian white wine that wasn't bad at all. In one of the trees above the house lived a Great Horned owl. David told us that he has lived in that tree for at least fifteen years. That was one of the few nights a year when he wasn't alone. He shouted a few times from somewhere in the dark to let us know, or maybe he was just cursing his own God.

The temperature dropped to minus twelve. However, everything resisted with dignity, the plants, the insects, the small mammals, the birds. We watched while staying in the warmth of the house. One evening I took a look at YouTube trends, I heard the most played music at the moment and I didn't know anything about it, not a name, not a title, a bit like footballers after a few years of not watching matches anymore and it suddenly seems like they have made up names. It feels like everyone is moving on without you. But are they really moving forward? And where to? And what is there, where everyone is going, in such a hurry? What were they promised? It seems to me that no one is very clear about this. It seems to me that there is a general nervousness, a throng. There is something in front of them, but what? What if there was nothing? What if it was just a gimmick, a giant treadmill? So I'm just sitting here, waiting. It is a gentle desert, but I have found my happiness here. Although it is very difficult to remain happy without the guarantee of a future reward, of a God or who knows who. So it's always better for me to get busy for some reason yet to be determined.

Every now and then, before darkness fell, in the hottest hours even if only in a manner of speaking, I walked around. I thought of a love that ended and perhaps I told myself that it had never begun because true love does not end and goes beyond the boundaries of human nonsense and I am afraid of those who claim the opposite. In front of a puddle of water, I listened to *Into My Arms* by Nick Cave and I thought of a girl I had really loved and for that reason I would love forever and I felt that I could fall in love again, with another person. I started to make room for that eventuality and then I kicked a pebble which landed in a puddle and sank. The pool was infested with a strange species of pointy snails. I didn't check on the internet what snails they were because I felt like I was cheating, like breaking the magic of their mystery. I regretted it a bit: now, however, it is impossible for me to remember their exact shape and to see them again I would have to travel forty hours and spend two thousand euros, or get a degree in biology. In both cases it's not worth it.

Here I look like a ninja, a pirate or a terrorist. I surely don't look like a director. Maybe I'm not, maybe I never have been and maybe I never will be. Maybe this is a great fortune or maybe it will be my downfall. Come to think of it, it's already my second life. During the first one I was a gamer, I played a lot of matches, I won tournaments, they knew me. Obviously this was before everything became a business and you could make a salary. If I have a timing it's to start too early and stop when things start to get better. Who knows if I'll stop making films, if I'll just make one, ten or a hundred. Alternative lives that I wouldn't mind: a craftsman's workshop, working with wood or ceramics; a restaurant in the Alps; working in the secret services out of curiosity to see with my own eyes the horrifying mechanism by which the world works; open a school; be a musician. Who knows how it will end.

Michael is David's oldest friend. A tall, thin man, with blue eyes, a handsome, hollow face to which age has been kind and a ringing, hoarse voice. His house is a few hundred meters from David's, following a path through bushes of artemisia tridentata, burning wrecks of old pickups and giant iron sculptures that I later discovered were by his wife. His house was built with poorer materials, it was mainly made of sheet metal and had three separate buildings, the main one with a kitchen, a very large living room, a couple of bedrooms and a bathroom, then a garage and finally a shed which was Michael's studio on whose walls hung dozens and dozens of works, mainly desert and minimalist landscapes. Michael talked a lot, perhaps too much, he really had an iron memory, so much so that David was worried that once in the scene he might talk without stopping and in fact it was a problem that we had to face. He spoke above all of his many dogs, his houses and his cars, but above all of his dogs and of a specific dog of which he had been very fond because he was particularly intelligent. He gave me one of his books. It was very badly laid out, the cover was a photograph of the desert divided into three by the folds of the paperback binding, but the internal pages were truly beautiful, a handwritten diary with very dense pen writing, all around the drawings of his cars, his houses and his dogs. He immediately made the impression on me of a man who could become attached to everything and everyone very quickly and who had freed up as much space as possible within himself to store as many memories, names, places and animals as he could, and for that very reason he had never had time to learn how to make book covers, because who cares anyway.

In October 1978, David and Michael got lost in the Owyhee Desert. Twenty-four hours earlier David was in a suit and tie talking about business in a New York skyscraper and at that moment, while they were taking a drive, the car broke down and left them stranded in the middle of nowhere. Going back along the path on foot was a terrible idea, it would have taken days and days, and the nearest town was a few dozen kilometers away but they would have had to travel through the desert. At the time they had a very generic map, 250,000:1, which was really difficult to orient yourself on. They got lost. Furthermore, David, going down a slope, became lame. They spent the night outside in the frost, under a clear sky full of stars. They looked death in the face. The next day, without eating or drinking, they followed a metallic sound to a gas pumping station. There they saw a truck with workers, they ran at breakneck speed and were saved. The workers brought them peanut butter sandwiches and told them they only came to that station once a month and only for two hours. They had been lucky. It is very easy to die, after all it is enough not to breathe for a few minutes, not to drink for a few days, not to piss for about twenty hours or not to eat for a week. Every second we fight with death without realizing it too much, and this is what man is: not taking things too seriously, not like rabbits, or deer, or birds, that's why we screwed up the food chain. The world's fuel is arrogance, there are those who have little and those who have a lot and you can immediately understand who's who from where they end up. When they told me this story I thought that this film exists only because the employee who took the shifts of the workers at the pumping station in October 1978 saw fit to send people there that day. Otherwise David and Mike would probably be dead, nothing would be known about them, there would be no map collection, no film, there wouldn't be these sentences and who knows what I was doing now. On one of the walls of the desert house, David hung the map of the Owyhee Desert. The world is strange and dances.

Was it the camera that transformed me into a director, or was it I, the director, who transformed the camera into an eye, into a brain, into a memory? Is this perhaps a symbiosis or a case of parasitism? Are we like the crab and the anemone or like the hyenas and the vultures? It's not always clear to me whether I like the camera or not. Sometimes I feel like it's a huge boulder to move. I would like it to be incorporeal or integrated. I have a feeling it will happen soon and then it will be fun or it will be the end of cinema. We shot a film as if it were a geographical atlas, or a picture story. It certainly doesn't feel much like a movie. For me this is an advantage, but for many it is a flaw. If I knew how to give a fuck, I would be easier on myself.

I feel guilty about strange things. For example, for this track left by David's Jeep on the white sand of the Smoke Creek Desert. It was I who planned that scene and because of my choice we disturbed that expanse of pure white with muddy rubber streaks. I felt like I had ruined some God's Zen garden and, once I got home, I thought about it for a long time before falling asleep, as if anticipating some deserved punishment. On the other hand, if that sense of guilt had been perfectly useless, why did it develop during billions of years of evolution? It certainly can't just serve to enrich psychotherapists, otherwise it would all be very depressing and I would have done everything wrong and all good things would mean absolutely nothing.

Recording sound is like transforming yourself for a period of time into a different animal, with owl-like hearing, it means feeling somehow on the hunt, a hunt disinterested in the flesh, but hungry for a sort of sonic ether, crunchy and otherworldly . It's a real transmutation. When we are no longer just men, but half men and half devices, will they sell similar contraptions? Peregrine falcon glasses, shark noses, wolf tongues? I think if we had the same kind of amplification in our taste buds and nose that headphones and booms offer to our hearing we would go for the jugular for the sake of tasting each other. It would be a bloodbath. Best not to say these things out loud in Palo Alto. Some crazy person would start looking for angel investors right away.

As I fell asleep looking out that window, at the blue desert under the moonlight, I understood why that place brought me such tranquility. Quite simply there was less of the world. Usually there was too much of it out there, an unmanageable, gigantic world, full of nonsense but also full of mysteries and wonders and a single life is a gigantic joke that can go in billions of different directions, it takes a good nerve to think you're really important and yet if you don't have that nerve you fall into a terrifying abyss. Not falling is a miracle, nothing other than a miracle, a fragile and dazzling hallucination, a balancing act, a circus, a dance, pure madness. Reason doesn't exist. I fell asleep and forgot about it.

It was time to leave the desert too. Of the scenes we shot, we didn't cut a single one. This meant I was putting things into focus. As the house disappeared around the corner of the driveway, looking back, I wondered if I would ever see that place again. A feeling similar to when I said goodbye to my grandmother on her hospital bed, before she died, and I asked myself the same thing knowing full well that the answer was no, I would never see her again. I formulated a desire within myself to have a home too, a home of my own, one day. I would have had to really sweat it out and the sweat wouldn't have been enough, I also needed a bit of luck and less inflation. We went back to sleep in the house in San Francisco for just one night, I explored it once again as if it were a large cetacean, a breathing organism. I had shot my first film in that place. Could I believe it? I had wanted it so much and had almost finished it. Had all this happened because I had expressed the desire to do so, or by pure chance? Are the forces of the world organized to respond to our most intimate dreams? In doubt, I made a couple of other wishes. I went down to the basement, took one last look at the maps, then took a shower and went to sleep.

The next morning we had a plane to Halifax, then a night in the airport hotel, then a six hour drive to Cape Breton Island , even if there was some construction on the road it wasn't like in Italy where construction means day long queues, we proceeded quickly towards Mabou, then from there we went straight towards MacKinnons Brook, just enough time to stop for groceries in a Canadian supermarket with a fish counter where there were real sea monsters and at every corner you were stopped by shop assistants who gave away really delicious butter biscuits, but I felt rude for taking more than two. Groceries for three, for the following week, were $667.50. Too much.

Here on Cape Mabou, in MacKinnons Brook, between October and November there is a period of time they call fly season. The wind is so strong that flies take shelter in the wood of the houses, slip into cracks and holes and lay their eggs there. The eggs hatch and they come in by the thousands. Although sticky traps were attached to the windows, the number of flies in the house was reminiscent of biblical plagues. Even when you thought you had killed them all, if you looked carefully at the floor, you could see the flies coming out of the holes in the wood, you could see them return, countless, before your eyes, as in a kind of inexplicable curse. We spent a large amount of time during the day killing them, also because they disturbed the audio, disturbed sleep, disturbed everything. The only way not to hear them was to turn off all types of lights so as to make them blind and unable to fly. I was so repelled by it that I didn't think that a scene where David tried to swat flies and never managed to get rid of them would be a great scene, but I'm only thinking about it now, it's too late, the movie's out and I'm an idiot. One managed to make it: while David is in the bathtub and hears the sounds of the bear outside rummaging in the organic bin, a fly flutters in front of his eyes and distracts him. Reality is always more powerful than fiction. It will find a way to end up in the film at all costs. This is a lesson that I learned late and that I should have learned sooner and if I had done it now the flies would be a fundamental character in the third part of the film and it would have been better. Or maybe they would distract me and I would end up making a mess.

As always, I stayed home to organize the footage, subtitle it, fit together the clips, try to complete the puzzle, or rather the atlas that we had tried to draw while making that film. Antonio and David walked along the web of paths that David had made together with a local association, then they sent me some selfies from the top, I smiled, swatted a fly and went back to editing. A bear lived in the area and I was fucking scared of it, denying to myself that the it was much more scared than me and moreover it was a male, so it would have minded its own business, it had no cubs or other nonsense to protect, in short nothing would have happened, but I imagined meeting him around every corner because I am convinced that everything you can imagine does not happen and that life wants to be unexpected at all costs and sometimes I have the habit of imagining things on purpose so as to cross them out of the list of possibilities and it usually works. In fact Antonio and David were not devoured. But they didn't have this paranoia. Every time Antonio could see far away instead of thinking about the bear he took a photo like this.

The house was full of portraits that were a hundred years old or more. David had no idea who they were, he had found them inside when he bought that house from the last heiress of this fishing family who had moved elsewhere, among the last to leave the ghost village of MacKinnons Brook, which once had a food shop, school and post office and now it no longer existed, nature had eaten it and those nameless faces that someone had hung on the wall because they loved them and wanted to save them from oblivion were still there, although nameless, so love had worked but only halfway. Perhaps influenced by all those faces, Antonio framed himself in the mirror in this self-portrait. Perhaps the elementary particles will retain the memory of this shot forever, but the rest will forget about it. Perhaps a traveler, passing through MacKinnons Brook, one day when the house will be an abandoned ruin, will pass in front of this dusty mirror and for a second, out of the corner of his eye, he will think he saw a man in the mirror taking a photo. But he will tell himself that it was a simple impression, he will spit on the ground and move on.

4x4

We were about to shoot the only moving shot in the entire film that wasn't constructed in post-production. David had told me about a recurring dream of his in which he walked along that long path in the woods to get to the house in MacKinnons Brook. It was a very mysterious dream and full of a gentle restlessness, the kind that not only hides disastrous thoughts, but also sweet sensations. Obviously, since there were only two of us we didn't have the right means to do it, so we decided to put the tripod on the back of Roddie's pickup like you do when you make a short film in high school and you don't have any money and we prayed, because the terrain was very rough and we feared it would came out badly. Antonio wanted to secure the tripod with ropes but we had neither the ropes nor studied how to tie knots that made sense. Two idiots as per the twenty-first century textbook. Roddie - who was a forester and a fisherman and killed mice and flies and cut wood and laid out the path and did little plumbing jobs and kept the water pipes from freezing and checked the antenna dish and knew how to build wood structures, dig wells, fix electrical cables, call birds with his hands and who knows how many other devilry things that have been forgotten or perhaps purposely deleted from an era that wants us to be as needy as possible - Roddie in short offered to give us a hand. Roddie's hand was gigantic, it was a shovel, if a bear had hands instead of paws it would have Roddie's hands, they were full of nerves, dry and hard, and instead of being cylindrical the fingers were square like parallelepipeds and the lines of the skin ran along their surface like crevasses, what's more they were full of thick white hairs, they were hands ready for anything. In fact, he took two ropes, tied them to the tripod and the pickup and by God, the tripod wouldn't have moved even with a meteorite. The shot came out better than a steadycam. I didn't even have to stabilize it in post-production. I thought to myself, they screwed us, they didn't teach us anything, I didn't learn these things and now I don't know how to build a house, I don't know how to look after myself, I'm at the mercy of Capitalism, I only know how to make films. So of course I continued making the film.

*A Stranger Quest* was practically finished. The ending was missing, but we would have shot it soon. We knew how to do it and all. We were very relaxed and shot very little time per day. We ate well and slept equally well. We visited a friend of David's who gave us blueberry muffins that I will remember for a lifetime and black tea that made your veins pop out of your eyes. On the large corner window in her living room she had attached stickers of swallows which, glued like this, would never go anywhere. Neither would she, who loved Mabou but whose mind certainly flew away every now and then. She had a very affectionate cat who was afraid of the tripod and spent those two hours in eternal indecision, whether to overcome the metal monster and be cuddled or stay on his own business and avoid trouble. Obviously he chose the latter like all cats. They remembered their old friend Jim together, then she gave David a map. It was map number 175,745 in his collection. It was snowing at times, and these were the harbingers of winter that would soon arrive and bury everything under a white blanket. Everything had gone well. I wanted to make a film about the Pillars of Hercules and this is definitely a film about the Pillars of Hercules. I wanted to make a sweet and silent film, tender and sincere, about what it means to dedicate your life to something, and I think I did it.

Taking a path through the vegetation that crosses a couple of streams you arrive at an open space with the little house that David built twice, once when he was twenty and the wind took it away and again when he was twenty-four or twenty-five, which was done better. He and his friend had saws, nails, a hammer and wood and a manual on how to build houses that was a gift from his grandfather. They slept in tents and started again in the morning. Jim brought him sandwiches and cold water. The house was still there, he told us, because it had a triangular shape with the tip towards the cliff, so the wind slipped around it and went to tear apart other houses. In reality, Antonio took this photo on his way back, and not on the way in. In fact we had come to the house from above, from a wider road that a hundred years earlier was the main road of MacKinnons Brook. David took us in front of some bushes and told us: there were some houses there; but absolutely nothing could be seen. The main road reached the little house from above, then ended in a precipice overlooking the Atlantic. When I saw it I gasped because it looked like the last house in the world. Then I said to myself: this is a thought that no longer makes any sense, even if it once would have. In fact, the earth was spherical, three thousand kilometers away there was Ireland and the absurd thing is that I wished I didn't know it, that I wanted to forget everything I knew about geography to believe in some magic again.

Inside the house, about twenty square meters, there was a gas kitchen, a refrigerator, a bedroom, a mezzanine where another mattress could fit, a bathroom with a bathtub, a wood stove, a table and a rocking chair in front of a large window overlooking the ocean. The wind shook it very strongly and made the wooden boards creak. It felt like being inside a tree. The house, swept by the furious wind on all four sides, with that bitter cold, gave a sense of protection and almost maternal warmth, it made you want to make love inside it, and I thought of whoever founded a city, a village, at the pleasure of sitting for the first time in a little house like that after having built it and suddenly having a house from nothing, a shelter from the bears and the rain, from the insects and the thorns of the plants, and I thought what kind of pleasure they must have had, those bastards, a pleasure that I will never, ever experience, but just imagining it brings tears to my eyes.

Some views are sold as such, but they are just rip-offs. Others, however, teach you what a view is, restoring the sense of vastness that is released by a gaze that encounters nothing human at a long distance. From the little house the view was on the end of the world. What is the end of the world? It's where there's no more people, where there's no one left. Where our chatter isn't even chatter. Here I understood what I had come to do and that the film was over. To go further you had to be a bird or a landslide but if you were a landslide you wouldn't have gone too far. In any case I was a human being and I had to stop there. There were no ships and there were no planes. There was just nothing at all. For sixty years David had been making this entire journey simply to sit in his rocking chair, and then stay there for a while without doing anything, thinking about all the time that had passed and wondering what it meant and what wonder and what mystery it all was.

I didn't know that Antonio had taken this photo. If I remember correctly, I had just called the end of shooting the movie and I was crying. Antonio didn't, and neither did David. This meant that this film was ultimately my film. It would never have happened without them, but the fate that that film had sealed was mine. What had I done? Had I really made a film? So? We hugged each other, closed the house tightly and went home to eat. That was it. I had made a film and life continued as if nothing had happened, digestion, breathing, sleep, and all. The rice with broccoli still tasted like rice with broccoli, the water tasted like water, the cold was still cold and the wind whistled like a beast as if to say: do what you want, sooner or later I'll tear this house down. Somewhere the bear was probably scratching its ass on the bark of a tree and then going into hibernation. It was time to return home from a strange journey.

We departed MacKinnons Brook on November 20, 2022 at 9am. We had slept well, everything was ready and it was snowing lightly. David accompanied us to the Halifax airport and there I had a dollar bill signed as a souvenir of the trip. While we were going through security they took my backpack with the laptop and asked me to open it. As I lifted the screen, a fly that had been stuck in there flew out. The plane left promptly at 4.35pm and the return journey seemed shorter like all return journeys.

David returned to MacKinnons Brook alone, to stay there for another week, alone, surrounded by nothing at all.

I would like to thank Il Varco, Marco, Marina, Marianna, Kubai Film in the person of Marco and Lucio, Antonio Morra, Antonio La Camera, Tommaso Barbaro and all the guys from Fullcode, Zhenia Kazankina, David Foster Wallace and Eiichiro Oda.
Thanks of course to David and Abby Rumsey.

Finished printing in 2024.
First edition.

Layout by Marina Rossi
Book design by Andrea Gatopoulos